• DEIRDRE COATES

At Home with Spelling 1

• Oxford University Press •

Note to parents

This series of spelling workbooks will teach your child to spell well, while having lots of fun! Here is some advice on how to work through the books:

- The books can be used either by your child working alone, or with your help in saying the words, discussing the spellings, finding rhyming words or common letter patterns.

- Children learn in different ways. Some learn from what they see, while others are more receptive to listening. The variety of activities in these books deliberately combines the learning modes of reading, writing, speaking and listening.

- Good spellers all have an awareness of how to link sounds and letters, how to blend groups of sounds together, and how to form syllables and words. The activities are therefore designed to develop rhyme and syllable awareness, and decoding skills, as well as visual perception.

- New spellings are introduced in groups that share a common letter pattern. Whenever there is a reason why words are spelt in a particular way, this reason is explained.

- Many of our most common words break the spelling rules. Such words are introduced throughout the books, to give children plenty of practice in reading and writing these anomalies.

- It is best to follow the order of the books, as they are planned to a highly systematic structure. Groups of words are introduced like bricks in a wall, a row at a time. Not only does this ensure that rules are introduced in a logical sequence, but also that the whole structure of the child's learning has a firm foundation.

Oxford University Press, Great Clarendon Street, Oxford OX2 6DP

Oxford University Press is a department of the University of Oxford. It furthers the University's objective of excellence in research, scholarship, and education by publishing worldwide in

Oxford   New York

Auckland   Cape Town   Dar es Salaam   Hong Kong   Karachi Kuala Lumpur   Madrid   Melbourne   Mexico City   Nairobi New Delhi   Shanghai   Taipei   Toronto

With offices in

Argentina   Austria   Brazil   Chile   Czech Republic   France   Greece Guatemala   Hungary   Italy   Japan   Poland   Portugal   Singapore South Korea   Switzerland   Thailand   Turkey   Ukraine   Vietnam

Oxford is a registered trade mark of Oxford University Press in the UK and in certain other countries

© Deirdre Coates 1997
First published 1997

ISBN-13: 978 0 19 834169 7

20 19 18 17 16 15 14 13 12 11

Typeset and designed by Oxprint Design, Oxford
Illustrations by Ray and Corrine Burrows

Printed in Hong Kong

Contents

The alphabet

Write the small letters.

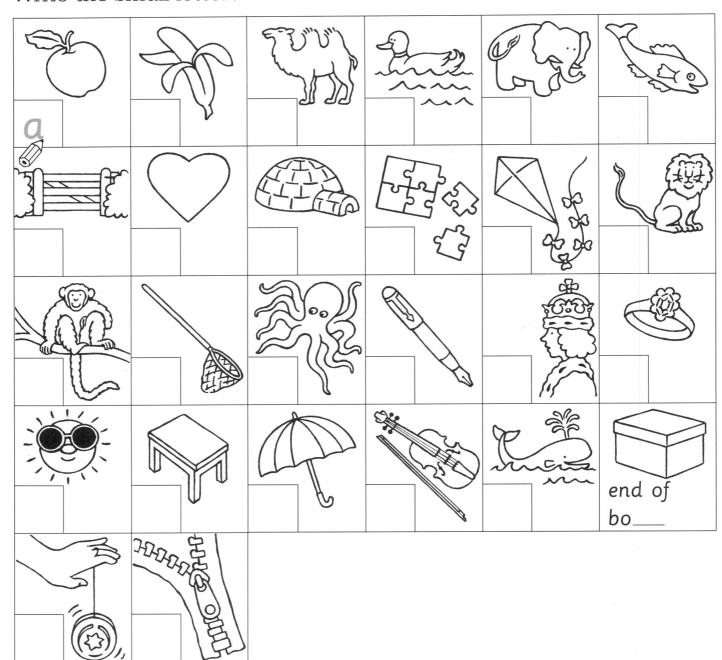

a

end of
bo____

aA bB cC dD eE fF gG hH iI

jJ kK lL mM nN oO pP qQ

rR sS tT uU vV wW xX yY zZ

Alphabetical order

Fill the gaps.

Now write the alphabet in capital letters.

Now write the alphabet in capital letters.

Fred   Ann   Harry   Jan   Dan   Kim   Ben   Mary

List the children in alphabetical order.

1 _____   5 _____

2 _____   6 _____

3 _____   7 _____

4 _____   8 _____

Vowels

a e i o u

These five letters are called vowels.

Ring the vowels in these words.

w(i)g	bat	pen	hut	hot
pit	pat	pet	pot	put
pan	pin	sit	set	sat
fox	fix	mad	bad	bid
bed	bud	cot	nut	fun

Fill the gaps with vowels.

b__g   b__g   b__g

b__g   b__g

Fill in the vowel

a e i o u

s__m

f__n

l__g

c__p

p__n

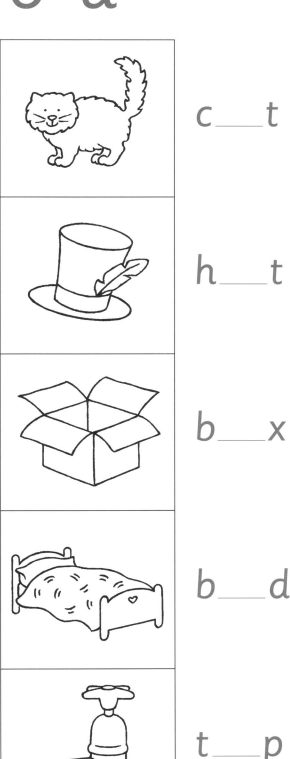

c__t

h__t

b__x

b__d

t__p

Consonants

All the letters that are not vowels are called consonants.
Ring the consonants below.

a   ⓑ   c   d   e   f   g   h   i

j   k   l   m   n   o   p   q   r

s   t   u   v   w   x   y   z

Write in the first consonant to change

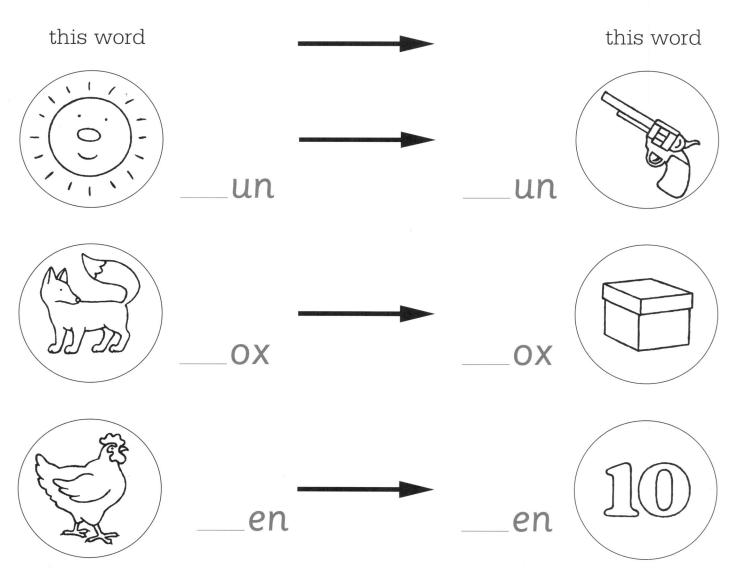

this word   ⟶   this word

___un   ___un

___ox   ___ox

___en   ___en

Consonants

Write in the last consonant to change

this word   this word

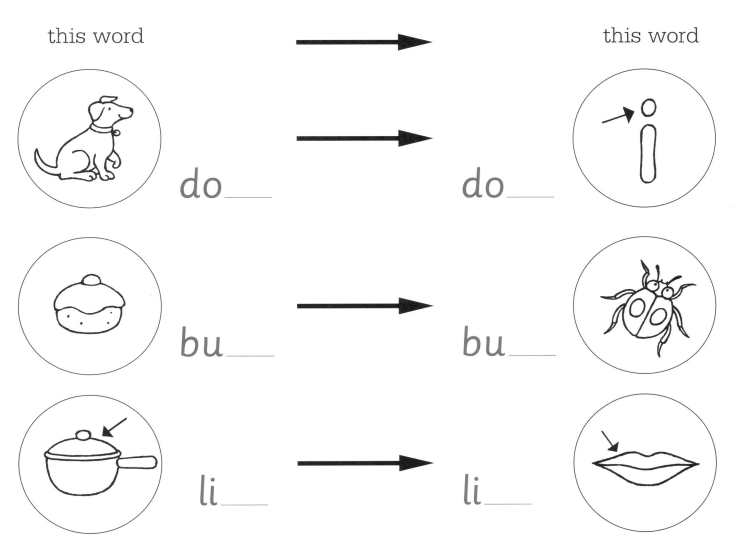

do___   do___

bu___   bu___

li___   li___

The words in each group all end with the same consonant.
Write it in the box.

Join the rhymes

A rhyme makes the same sound at the end of the word, like *star* and *car*.

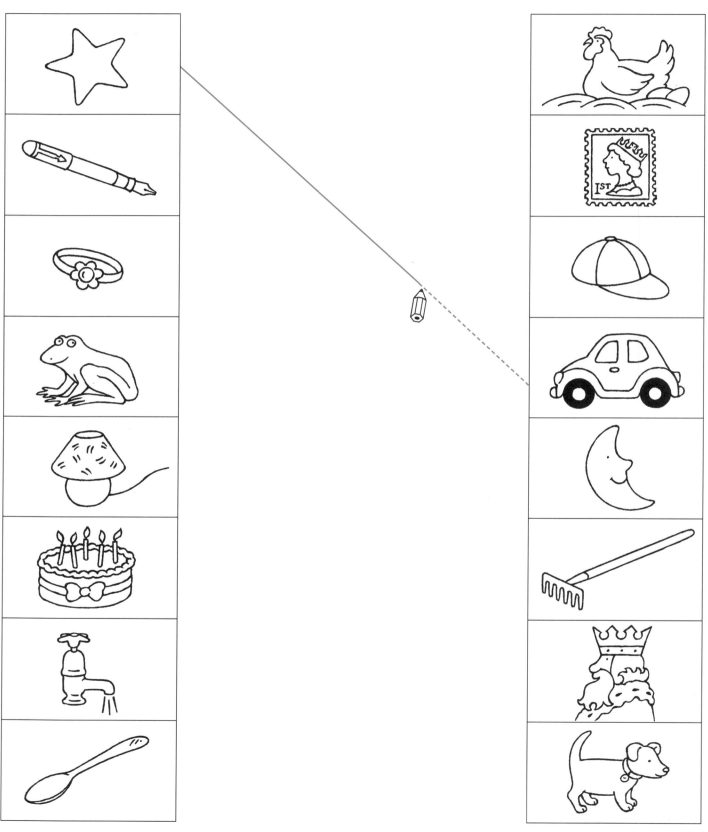

Hear the difference

log
long

thick
think

lip
limp

pump
pup

wig
wing

pond
pod

bed
bend

sad
sand

sick
sink

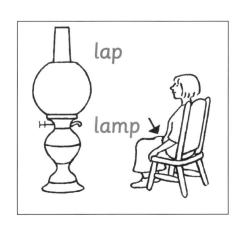

lap

lamp

truck

trunk

cap

camp

Two consonants, one sound

th   sh   ch

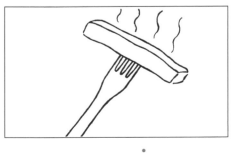

___ell   ___ur___   ___ree

___umb   ___ip   ___ick

___est   fi___   ba___

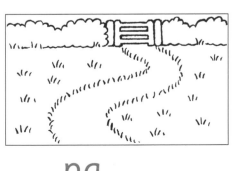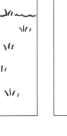

___ip   pa___   di___

12

Blended consonants

____ ock	____ oon	____ ove	____ ush
____ ate	____ ab	____ ack	____ am
____ ar	____ og	____ ing	____ arf
____ arf	____ ake	____ um	____ ide
____ enty	____ ee	____ ug	____ an
____ apes	____ y	____ oke	____ ee

bl   tr   sp   br   cl   fl   st   sl   sw   pr   dr   gr

tw   fr   dw   pl   sn   thr   sm   cr   sl   sc   gl

Double consonants

This is Flossy.
She has a frill on the cuff of her dress.

ff	ll	ss
off	bell	ass
cliff	fell	mass
sniff	well	chess
stiff	sell	dress
cuff	ill	mess
huff	hill	miss
stuff	will	cross
	pull	moss
	full	fuss
	bull	

Fill the gaps with words from the lists.

1 The boy _____ off the wall.

2 Hurry or you _____ _____ the bus.

3 I hope you get _____ soon.

4 The tall girl wore a red _____.

5 Don't _____. Use a hanky.

6 When the _____ rings it is time to go home.

14

all

Write the -all words in the balls.

tell   till   tall   fall   fill   fell
ill   all   will   wall   well   smell
small   hill   hall   hull   bull
ball   bell   bill   still   thrill   stall
cross   boss   fill   call   bull   full   pull

Fill the gaps in the poem

Bill   will   pull

mess

unwell   ill   cross

There was a girl whose name was Floss,

She always made her mother _____.

A jar with ink she tried to fill,

Then gave the jar to baby _____.

The toddler held the jar so full,

He gave it an enormous _____.

The ink splashed all down Floss's dress.

And made a really awful _____.

It covered every little frill,

And made her mother feel quite _____.

More tales of Flossy I could tell,

But they would make you feel _____.

So Flossy is a bad girl still,

She always was and always _____.

16

ff ll ss

Fill the gaps.

a _____ on a _____

a _____ on a _____

a _____ on a _____

_____ the door _____

a _____ on a st_____

a _____ on a _____

someone _____

and someone _____

sp_____ the water

onto the _____

a _____ with

a _____

ar

Write the ar words in the car.

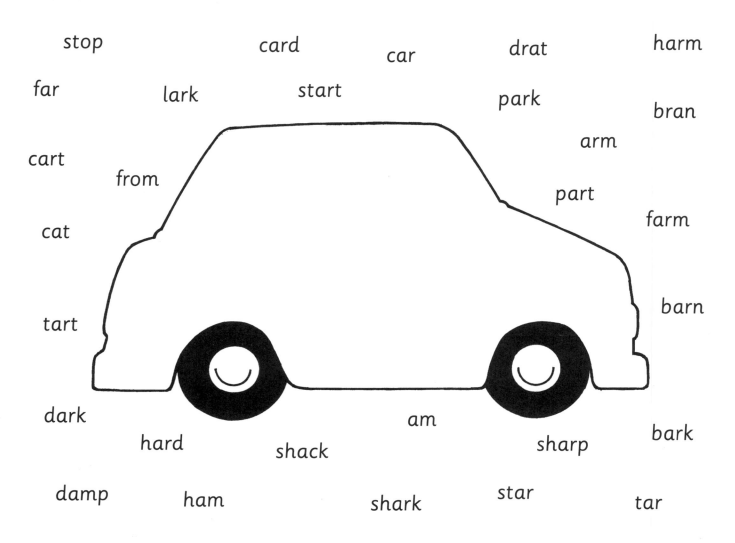

stop   card   car   drat   harm

far   lark   start   park   bran

arm

cart   from   part   farm

cat

tart   barn

dark   am   bark

hard   shack   sharp

damp   ham   shark   star   tar

Fill the gaps with words from the car.

1 Dogs often _____ at strangers.

2 Snap is a good _____ game.

3 It is too _____ to walk so we will go by _____.

4 A _____ is a big fish with _____ teeth.

18

or

Colour the or words in the fort.

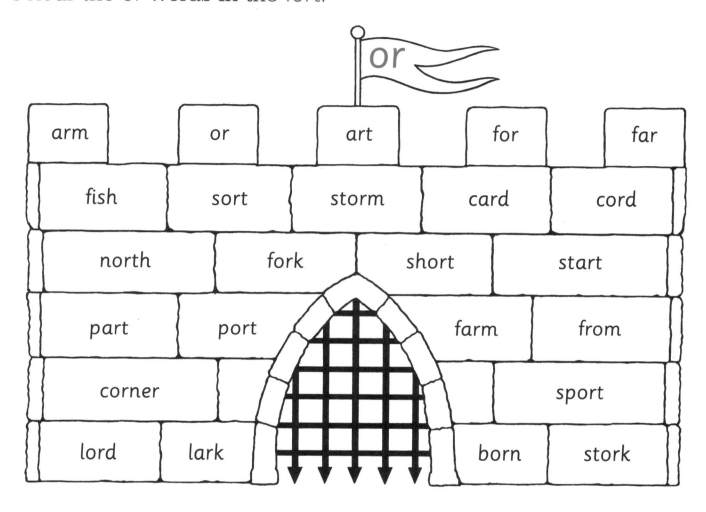

Fill the gaps with or words.

1 The _____ I like best is football.

2 The day I was _____ was the first day of my life.

3 Will you have pasta _____ pizza?

4 I ran around the _____ to the shop.

5 The _____ pole is all ice and snow.

ar riddles

1 I am land used for growing crops and keeping animals and I rhyme with *arm*.

2 I am a big fish with sharp teeth and a black fin that sticks above the water. I rhyme with *dark*.

3 I twinkle in the night sky and rhyme with *car*.

4 I am the opposite of soft and I rhyme with *card*.

5 I am where you begin and I rhyme with *cart*.

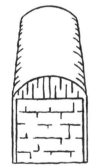

6 Farmers keep hay in me and I rhyme with *darn*.

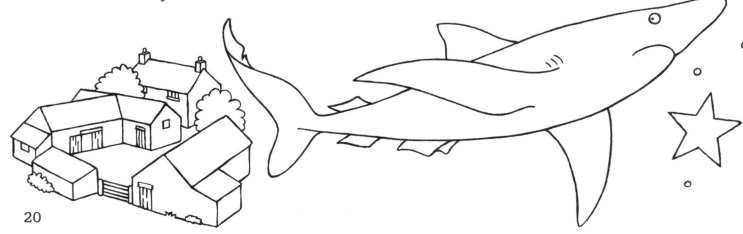

20

ar or or

Ring the right word.

1 The ship is in the [part   port].

2 My [car   cor] is very fast.

3 The [stors   stars] twinkle in the [dark   dork].

4 You dig in the [gorden   garden] with a [fork   fark].

Fill the gaps.

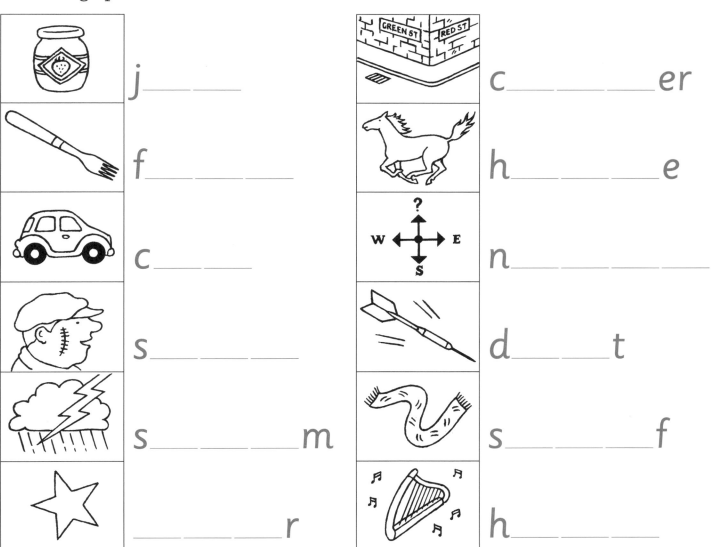

j_____

f_____

c_____

s_____

s_____m

_____r

c_____er

h_____e

n_____

d_____t

s_____f

h_____

Syllables

A syllable is a beat in a word. Frog has 1 beat; rabbit has 2 beats.

More syllables

  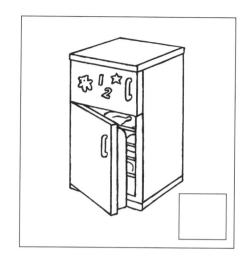

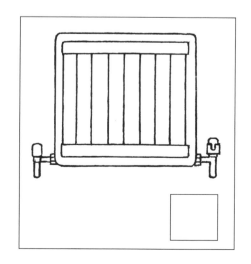  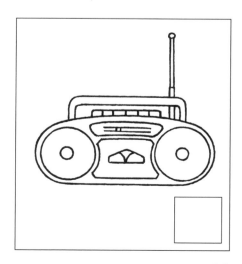

Sorting syllables

Sort out these syllables to make real words.

por   im   tant

ly   den   sud

yes   day   ter

stan   un   ding   der

to   row   mor

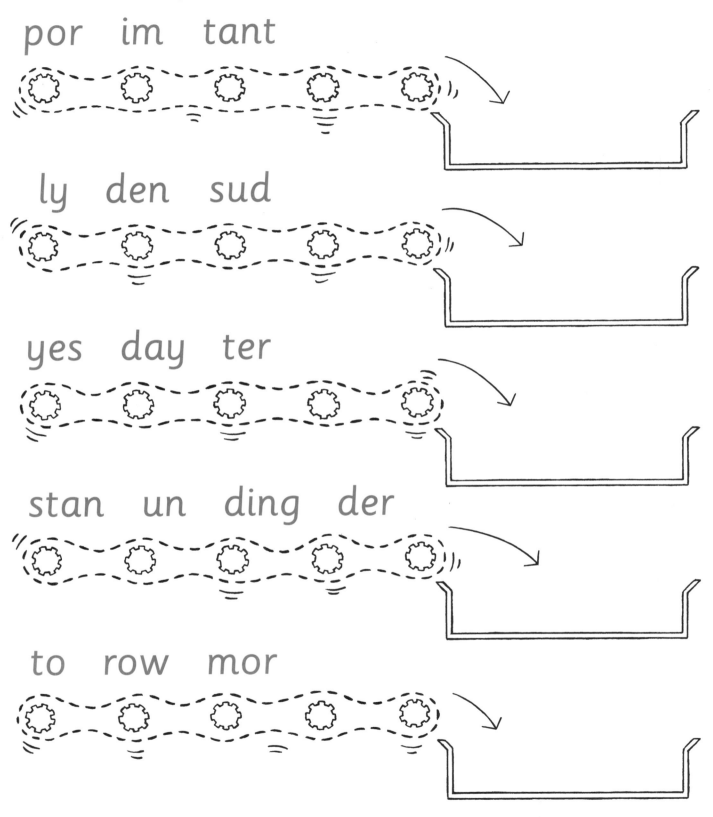

Word sums

Join up to make words of 2 syllables.

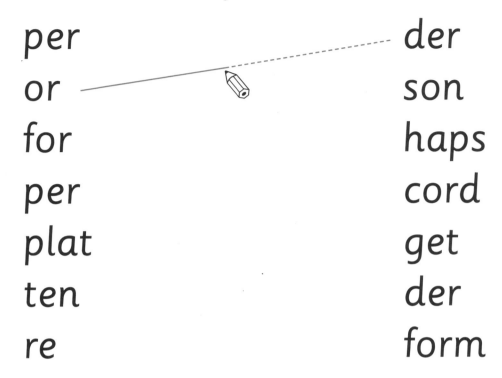

per	der
or	son
for	haps
per	cord
plat	get
ten	der
re	form

Add the two small words to make one bigger word.

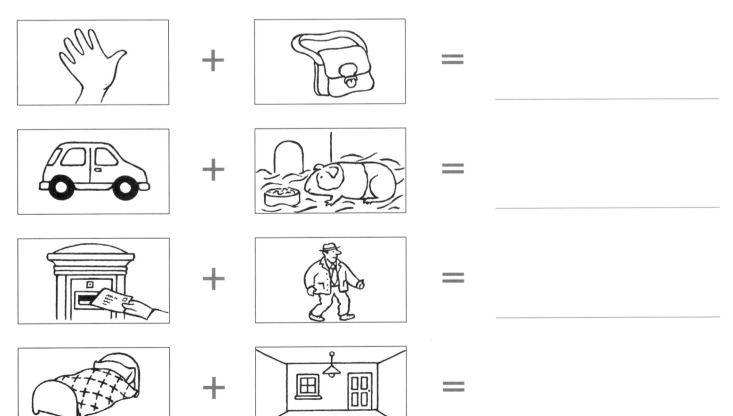

un-

Un- is a **prefix** added at the front of a word.
It makes the word mean *not*.
Write un- before these words. What do they then mean?

_____ well   _____ like   _____ happy

_____ safe   _____ fit   _____ tie

Ring the word which describes the picture.

happy   unhappy

well   unwell

fit   unfit

tied   untied

like   unlike

safe   unsafe

-S

Add *-s* to make a word *plural*, meaning more than one.

one cup   two cups

Write these *plural* words.

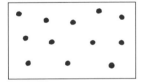 3 _____

 3 _____

 7 _____

 12 _____

 3 _____

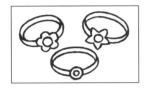 2 _____

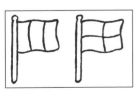 2 _____

 3 _____

 3 _____

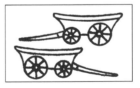 2 _____

 4 _____

 3 _____

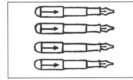 2 _____

 3 _____

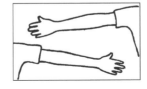 2 _____

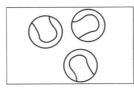 3 _____

-er

baker   player   scooter   golfer

diver   farmer   hiker   boxer

-er is a suffix, which means it comes at the end of a word.
Write in the words.

Add -er to make a new word.

A person who talks = a talker.   A person who farms = _____.

A person who jumps = _____.   A person who hunts = _____.

A person who sings = _____.   A person who plays = _____.

-er

ladder mother robber father

silver slippers hammer letter butter

Fill the gaps.

1 The _____ stole the gold and _____.

2 I like lots of _____ on my bread.

3 I put on my _____ as soon as I get home.

4 He went up the _____ and hit the tack with

his _____.

5 I live with my _____ and _____.

6 Today the postman brought me a _____.

-s

A *verb* is an action word, like *jump* or *run*. You add *-s* to verbs when you say *he jumps*, but *I jump*. Write in the verbs.

sleep

she _____

hop

the boy _____

think

he _____

look

the girl _____

sing

she _____

drink

she _____

run

the boy _____

sweep

he _____

sit

the lady _____

draw

the child _____

dig

the man _____

smile

the boy _____

jump

the frog _____

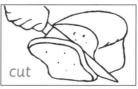
cut

the knife _____

chop

the axe _____

stand

the man _____

-ed

When the verb describes the *past*, we usually add *-ed*.
So, *I jump* today, but *I jumped* yesterday.
Fill the gaps by putting the verbs in the past with *-ed*.

I _____ out
of bed, and

_____ my
face and teeth.

I _____ my mum
to make breakfast,

and _____ out
my school books.

I _____ my
watch

and _____ to
the bus stop.

Because I _____
up at the sky on
the way

I _____ into
Jim,

and _____ on
the ground.

Jim _____
me to my feet,

_____ at me

and _____ if
I was OK.

31

-ing

-ing is another **suffix** which you can add to the end of verbs.
Mark off the -ing in these words.

drink|ing   jumping   sleeping

standing   winking   singing

Write the words under the pictures.

What are they doing?

1 What is the man in the chair doing? _____

2 What are the three children doing? _____

3 What is the man in the top hat doing? _____

4 What is the girl with curly hair doing? _____

5 What is the boy in the striped top doing? _____

6 What is the man in the flat cap doing? _____

7 What is the boy with short hair doing? _____

8 What is the girl doing to her teeth? _____

9 What are the two boys doing? _____

10 What is the boy at the sink doing? _____

W rule 1

A Witch called Wanda makes a
wa sound like *swan*.
Fill the gaps with these words.

wash   swan   want

what   swap   wand

wasp   watch   swallow

1 I wish I had a magic _____.

2 _____ do you _____?

3 You must _____ your hands before you eat.

4 Will you _____ your game for my book?

5 I tried to _____ it down in one gulp.

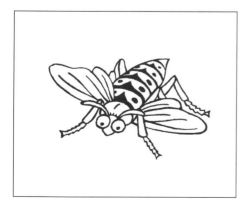

W rule 2

The Worst Witch makes
wor sound like *wer*.
Fill the gaps with these words.

worm   world

worse

worth   work

worthless   worthy

word

1 Do not say one more _____.

2 If you dig in the garden you may find a _____.

3 I must _____ hard at school.

4 A gold watch is _____ a lot.

5 I would like to travel all round the _____.

6 This food is _____ than it looks.

7 He is not _____ of such praise.

8 This rubbish is _____.

W rule 3

The Witch with a Wart makes war sound like wor.
Fill the gaps with these words.

swarm   war   towards   reward   dwarf   warm   warn

1   Help us to catch the robber and win a _____.

2   I was chased by a _____ of bees.

3   I _____ you, the food is disgusting.

4   We all prefer peace to _____.

5   I felt so _____ that I took off my jumper.

6   As the lion came _____ me I turned and ran.

7   Snow White's favourite _____ is Happy.

Want to warm up? Try changing **cold** into **warm** in this cool word tower!

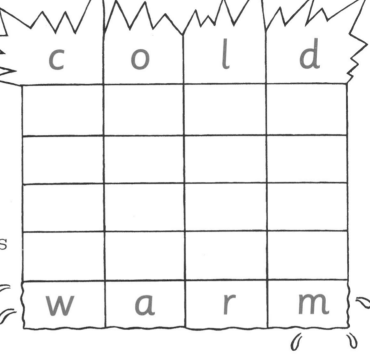

Another word for rope

Thick paper

Pulled by a horse

A small lump that sometimes grows on hands

Now try these dwarf words

1 A room in a hospital
2 A crowd of bees
3 The opposite of cool
4 A prize for doing something good
5 One of Snow White's seven friends
6 To tell someone of possible danger

1	w	a	r	
2	w	a	r
3	w	a	r
4		w	a	r
5	w	a	r
6	w	a	r	

37

saw

saw has the same letters as was, but they mean different things.
Write saw in the gaps.

1 We _____ that film last week.

2 You _____ him, didn't you?

3 In the park we _____ lions
and tigers and bears.

was or saw

Fill the gaps with was or saw.

1 He _____ only a baby when I

last _____ him.

2 I _____ the kitten run down the street.

3 She _____ too shy to sing.

4 The teacher _____ Jim pinch Ben

when he _____ trying to do his work.

# of or off

1 I went to the shop for a bag _____ buns.

2 Get _____ my bike this minute.

3 Because _____ you we are in a big mess.

4 I took the pack _____ cards _____ the table.

5 The dog fell _____ the cliff but he was not hurt.

6 He saw a flock _____ sheep and a herd _____ cows.

7 The bucket was full _____ water when he pushed it _____ the wall.

one

Join each word to its shape.

someone

noone

one

everyone

anyone

Fill the gaps. Watch for capital letters!

1 _____ two, three, and off we go.

2 _____ has stolen my bag.

3 _____ can get in because the door is locked.

4 Does _____ want this cake?

5 _____ is here so we can begin.

6 I looked and looked but _____ was there.

7 She is so kind that _____ likes her.

Common words

Finish the words to find out what each picture is saying.

Can I play
w____ y____ ?

I h____ cut
m__ h____ .

C____ h____
this minute!

T____ is all I
c____ find.

I fell i__ t____
pond a____ got
all wet.

I w____ a jar o__
jam a__ s____
plums.

Can I h____
o__ of those?

G__ m__
y____ money.

I l____ m__ frogs.

How to remember hard words

Help yourself remember how to spell hard words by
learning silly sentences like these.

because = big elephants can always understand small elephants

friend — i to the end will be your friend

said — silly Alice is dancing

laugh — little ants usually get hysterical

people — please enter on pretty little elephants

does — dogs only eat sausages

Can you make up more silly sentences for hard words?

Queen q is very grand and always has u to carry her train.

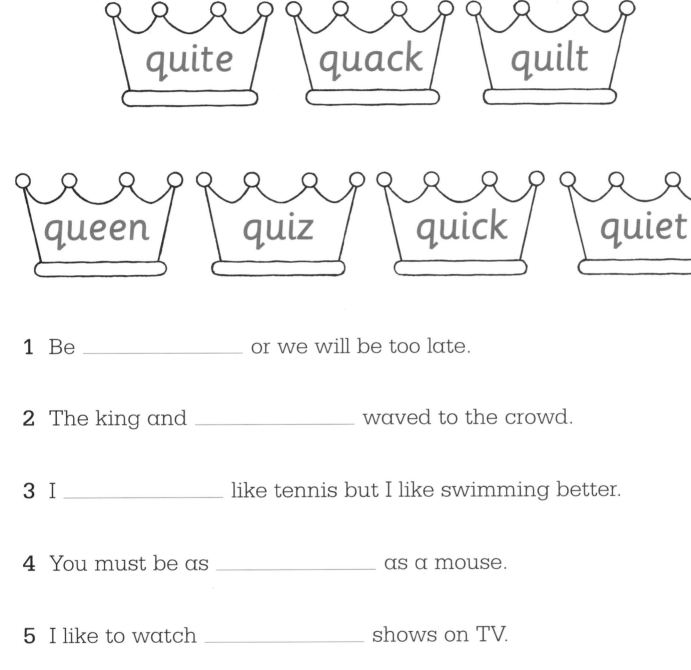

quite quack quilt

queen quiz quick quiet

1 Be _____ or we will be too late.

2 The king and _____ waved to the crowd.

3 I _____ like tennis but I like swimming better.

4 You must be as _____ as a mouse.

5 I like to watch _____ shows on TV.

6 On my bed I have a red and green _____.

7 Birds say tweet and ducks say _____.

Read the message and draw the picture

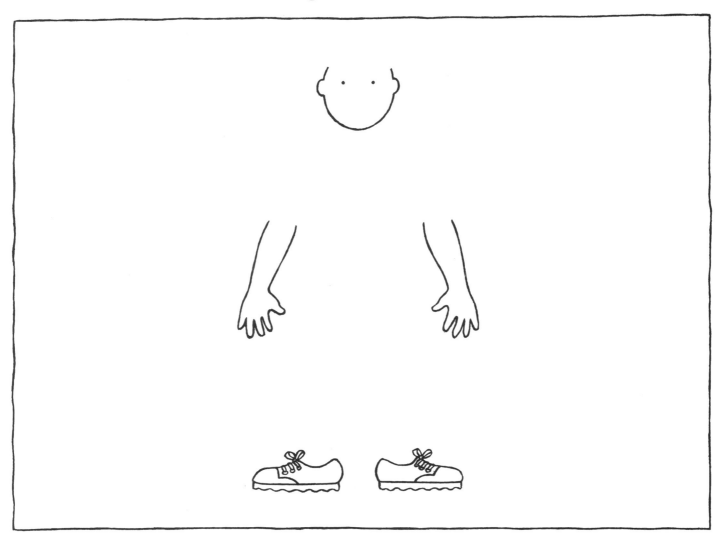

Charles has d🐱 hair 🖐 a st🚗 on his T-shirt. He 🎩s

a s🚗 on his ch🗑. He 🎩s 🛏r 🐜p . He 🎩s teeth

l🚲 a sh🍽 🖐 a long 🎵 n🌹. His eyes are f🚗

apart. In his left 🖐 is a g🌳n 🍯c 🖐 on his neck is

a p🥤 s🚗f .

44

W  ed [castle] Robbery

Help [bus] [acorn] find [pig]e [log]e B[hen]. He [hat]s a [br bed] beard [hand] a [nail]k [car] 1 his right cheek. He [hat]s a [pig]b[n rose] with a [sp dot] 1 the [ear]. He [hat]s a [scratch]ch 1 his left eye, [hand] wears a [gr crown] [h cat]. He [hat]s a [g running man].

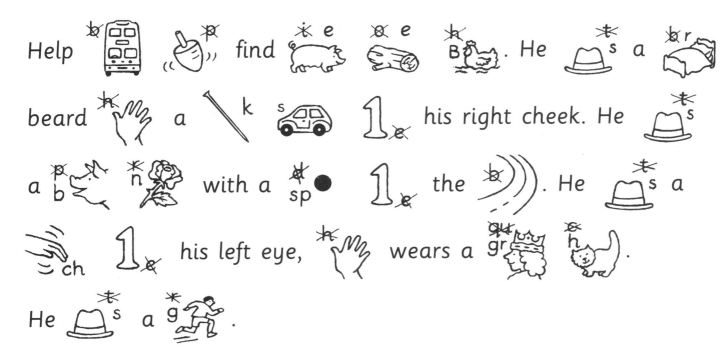

Word games

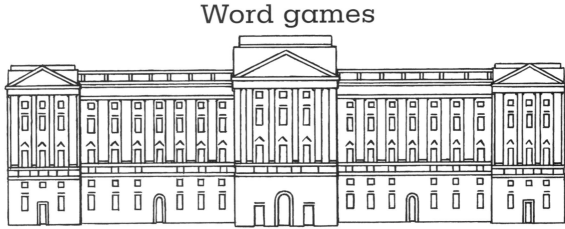

How many words can you find in BUCKINGHAM PALACE?
List them here.

_____

_____

_____

How many words can you
find in HIPPOPOTAMUS?

List them here.

_____

_____

_____

W sounds word-search

w	a	r	d	g	o	m	w	o	r	t	h	y	e	x
a	e	j	u	t	y	c	o	h	w	o	i	f	v	t
n	v	f	s	x	f	k	r	a	u	w	l	j	k	h
d	l	s	o	u	b	t	l	c	e	a	b	d	g	w
e	c	i	h	a	g	h	d	w	a	r	f	w	h	o
r	e	w	a	r	d	c	o	a	r	d	p	q	s	r
b	n	m	k	l	j	s	g	s	y	m	h	z	q	d
r	y	w	o	r	s	h	i	p	v	z	m	l	c	e
h	u	k	i	c	w	h	l	e	c	w	o	r	k	h
z	d	v	s	w	a	n	u	r	l	a	u	i	g	o
t	e	c	i	f	r	l	m	f	w	h	a	t	r	h
u	g	w	a	r	m	o	p	q	a	w	b	f	m	r
k	y	a	s	o	f	j	d	h	s	k	x	w	a	s
w	a	r	c	t	w	a	t	c	h	e	r	o	y	g
l	r	n	d	s	w	a	m	p	k	v	w	o	r	m

Find these words.

worm	ward	wash	was
word	worthy	watch	dwarf
work	reward	wasp	swan
what	wander	warm	
swamp	worship	toward	
war	swarm	warn	

Can you remember?

Fill the gaps in the words below.

b _ _ _ _	d _ _ _ _ f	_ _ el _ _	st _ _ _
f _ _ k	fi _ _ _	_ _ _ _ ee	b _ _ _ _
w _ tch	ba _ _ _	w _ _ _ _	s _ _ n
cu _ _ _	_ _ _ m	w _ _ ld	w _ _ d
2 fl _ _ _ _	c _ _ t	dr _ _ _ _	cr _ _ _ _
_ _ _ ack	h _ _ _ _	_ _ _ est	s _ _ _ _ f
_ _ _ een	mo _ _ _ _ _	3 _ _ am _ _ _	w _ _ m